Plants Activity Book

Author	Charlene Stout
Editor	Kathy Rogers
Illustrator	Barb Lorseyedi
Page Design	Linda Milliken
Cover Design	Imaginings

METRIC CONVERSION CHART

Refer to this chart when metric conversions are not found within the activity.

¼ tsp	=	1 ml	350° F	=	180° C
½ tsp	=	2 ml	375° F	=	190° C
1 tsp	=	5 ml	400° F	=	200° C
1 Tbsp	=	15 ml	425° F	=	216° C
¼ cup	=	60 ml	1 inch	=	2.54 cm
⅓ cup	=	80 ml	1 foot	=	30 cm
½ cup	=	125 ml	1 yard	=	91 cm
1 cup	=	250 ml	1 mile	=	1.6 km
1 oz.	=	28 g			
1 lb.	=	.45 kg			

EP117 • ©1998, 2003 Edupress, Inc.™ • P.O. Box 883 • Dana Point, CA 92629
www.edupressinc.com
ISBN 1-56472-117-5
Printed in USA

Table of Contents

Literature List

• **The Science Book of Things That Grow**
by Neil Ardley;
Harcourt 1991. (3-6)
With everyday equipment and step-by-step procedures, plant growth is explained.

• **Plants**
by Wendy Baker and Andrew Halsam;
Macmillan 1993. (3-6)
Concepts like photosynthesis are introduced and activities and experiments are provided.

• **Plants Without Seeds**
by Helen J. Challand;
Childrens 1986. (2-4)
Algae, bacteria, lichens, mosses, ferns, and fungi are included.

• **Plants**
by Anita Ganeri;
Watts 1992. (3-6)
In this British nature detective book, each section addresses one aspect, such as why plants have leaves.

• **Plants That Never Bloom**
by Ruth Heller;
Scholastic 1990. (1-3)
Creative descriptions of fungi, algae, lichen, moss, liverworts, ferns, horsetails, and other gymnosperm plants.

• **How a Seed Grows**
by Helene Jordan;
Harper 1992. (3-6)
A boy and girl plant and watch seeds grow.

• **Endangered Plants**
by Elaine Landau;
Watts 1992. (4-6)
Color photos enhance this look at plants in danger of extinction.

• **Dumb Cane and Daffodils: Poisonous Plants in the House and Garden**
by Carol Lerner;
Morrow 1990. (3-5)
An introduction to poisonous plants.

• **From Flower to Flower: Animals and Pollination**
by Patricia Lauber;
Crown 1987. (2-6)
How flowers are pollinated by insects and small animals, illustrated with stunning photographs.

• **Seeds: Pop, Stick, Glide**
by Patricia Lauber;
Crown 1991. (2-5)
An exploration of the many ways seeds travel.

• **Carnivorous Plants**
by Nancy J. Nielsen;
Watts 1992. (4-6)
A look with the help of color photos, at flesh-eating plants, such as the Venus flytrap.

• **Practical Plants**
by Joyce Pope;
Facts on File 1991. (4-8)
How people use plants for food, medicine, paper and cloth fiber, housing material, and pleasure.

• **George Washington Carver: Nature's Trailblazer**
by Teresa Rogers;
Twenty-first 1992. (2-5)
The life of the great black American agricultural chemist who discovered many new uses for peanuts, soybeans, and sweet potatoes.

• **A First Look at the World of Plants**
by Millicent E. Selsam;
Walker 1978. (3-6)
A simple description of the various groups of plants, with proper terminology.

• **Plant Experiments**
by Vera Webster;
Childrens 1982. (1-4)
A manual of simple experiments to be done with plants.

Glossary

bark—the outer covering of the trunk, branches and roots of a tree, usually hard and rough.

botany—the study of plants.

bud—a small swelling on a plant that grows into a leaf, a flower, or a branch.

bulb—the round underground part of plants such as onions, lilies, and tulips.

carnivorous—eating the flesh of animals (including insects).

chlorophyll—the substance that makes plants green. It enables plants to make food (sugar) from sunlight, carbon dioxide, and groundwater.

corm—like a bulb or tuber.

erosion—the slow wearing, blowing, washing, or eating away of soil by wind or water.

flower—the part of a plant that has colored petals and contains seeds to produce new plants; blossom.

fruit—the part of a plant that contains the seeds.

fungus—one group of plants that never bears flowers or leaves, is never green, and must live on other plants (mushrooms, molds, and mildews).

germination—process that causes plants to sprout and begin to grow.

grafting—to put a bud, branch, or shoot from one plant into a slit in another plant so the two pieces will grow together and form one plant.

grain—the seed of wheat, corn, rice, oats, and other cereal plants.

greenhouse—a glass-enclosed building for growing plants.

habitat—the place where a plant or animal lives and grows naturally.

hydroponics—the growing of plants in a nutrient (water/mineral) solution.

leaf—the flat green part of a plant that grows from a stem and produces the plant's food.

photosynthesis—the process of changing sunlight, water, and carbon dioxide into plant food.

pollination—the transfer of pollen (yellowish powder made in the anthers of flowers) from the stamen to the ovule of a flower.

propagation—the process by which more plants are started.

pruning—cutting out the dead or unwanted parts of a plant.

root—the lower part of a plant that grows down into the ground to hold the plant in the soil and to soak up water and minerals to feed the plant.

sap—a liquid that flows through the plant carrying water and food from one part to another.

seed—the part of a plant from which a new plant will grow.

spore—a tiny body that can grow into a new plant (as mushrooms and ferns).

stem—the part of the plant that supports the leaves and flowers. Water and food travel through stems to all parts of the plant.

tuber—like a bulb or corm.

weed—a plant that is harmful or useless and grows where it is not wanted.

wildflower—the flower of a plant that was not planted or cultivated by humans.

xylem—a tubelike system in the stems of plants that conducts water and minerals to other parts of a plant; also for storage of plant food and support of the stem.

Plant Products

Information

Plants supply the raw materials for many of mankind's most important needs—food, shelter, clothing, fuel, and medicines. The healthiest foods come from whole plants or parts of plants: fruits, vegetables from roots, stems, leaves and flowers, breads and cereals from grains and nuts. Coffee, tea, and soft drinks get their flavors from plants. Even meat and dairy products come from animals that could not survive without plants. Trees supply lumber and veneers for home-building and furniture. Wood is used for making paper products, cork, turpentine, and natural rubber. Clothing is made from the cotton plant or linen from flax. Rope is made from jute, hemp, and sisal plants. Around the world people use wood to heat their homes and cook their food.

Plants have been used to make medicines for hundreds of years. *Quinine* from the bark of the cinchona tree is used to treat malaria. *Digitalis* from the dried leaves of the foxglove plant is used to treat heart disease. *Penicillin* is a modern miracle drug made from a variety of tiny plants. Arthritis is treated with *cortisone* made from the roots of the Mexican yam plant. But many people would say the best thing about plants is the beauty and pleasure they derive from the sweet-smelling perfumes, the beautiful gardens, the waving fields of grain, or the tranquil quiet of a sleepy grove of trees.

Project

Search in desks and then in local grocery stores, categorizing items that are and are not made from plants.

Materials

- Lined paper
- Ruler
- Pencil

Directions

1. Use a ruler to divide a sheet of paper into two columns. Head the columns "MADE FROM PLANTS" and "NOT MADE FROM PLANTS."

2. Clean out classroom desks, listing each item under one of the two headings. Add to the lists with an assigned survey of grocery store shelves for plant and non-plant items.

3. Divide into small groups to debate whether the items listed are in the correct category. Draw some conclusions and report them back to the class, being ready to defend the choices made.

Amateur Botanists

Information

Botany is the study of plants. A botanist is a scientist who studies plants. They classify plants into "subkingdoms" according to their likenesses and differences. When people study botany they learn about the importance of plants and the many products they provide man and animals. Botanists can explain the role of plants in the cycle of nature as well as such terms as *photosynthesis*, *pollination*, and *propagation*. Plant scientists know all the different kinds of plants, the parts of a plant and how they function, where plants live, how they grow and change, and how they reproduce.

Project

- Create a Botanist's Journal to record all plant projects and and activities.
- Create a Gardeners' Newsletter.

Materials

- Paper
- Pencil
- Construction paper
- Stapler
- Crayons or markers

Botanist's Journal

1. Create a booklet by stapling a construction paper cover to a stack of several pieces of plain paper. Decorate the cover with crayons or markers and add the title, *Botanist's Journal.*

2. Date and write up daily entries in the journal. Keep track of all of your plant observations, experiments, and projects including notes for descriptions and news articles and your first sketches and diagrams.

Gardeners' Newsletter

Use journal entries to write up and publish *The Botanist Newsletter* with articles about your plant-related activities.

Photosynthesis

Information

Most living creatures need to breathe oxygen in order to stay alive. Without green plants there would be no oxygen on Earth! Green plants produce pure oxygen in a process called *photosynthesis* which means "making things with light." The plant's leaves capture the sun's light energy and use it to make the plant's food from carbon dioxide and water. As this happens molecules of oxygen are given off into the air.

Project

Conduct a water plant experiment to determine what gas is produced by photosynthesis.

Directions

1. Fill a bowl with water up to one inch (2.54 cm) from the top. Lay the pondweed in the bottom.

2. Lower the jar into the water on its side to fill it with water before turning it upside down over the plant.

3. Place the bowl in full sun for several hours until bubbles of gas form on the pondweed leaves and float upward, collecting in pockets on the glass jar.

4. Lift the jar and carefully turn it over so as to not disturb the bubbles.

5. Have an adult put a lighted match down into the jar. *Oxygen will burn brightly; carbon dioxide will smother the flame.*

6. Draw conclusions about the results of photosynthesis.

Materials

- Clear glass bowl
- Clear glass jar
- Water plant (available at aquarium supply stores)
- Clean water
- Long-stemmed match sticks

Plant Needs

Information

Each type of plant has its own particular set of needs in order to grow and flourish:

- Correct amounts of light
- Correct temperature
- Correct amounts of water and minerals
- Good supply of oxygen

Succulents need different conditions than water plants. A deficiency in any of the four above needs will cause the plant problems.

Project

Conduct simple plant experiments, varying conditions to learn what plants need to flourish.

Materials

- Plant Needs experiment page, following
- Camera
- Materials as listed in individual experiments

Directions

1. Divide the class into small groups. Photocopy the Plant Needs experiment page and cut apart on the solid lines. Give each group an experiment to conduct. Each group will need duplicate sets of materials.

2. Follow the directions on the experiment cards to determine how small changes in light, water, oxygen, and temperature can affect a plant's growth.

3. Photograph each stage of the experiment and write a short summary of each stage. Combine the photographs and descriptions to create a display.

4. After a few weeks, share the experiments and the conclusions drawn by each group.

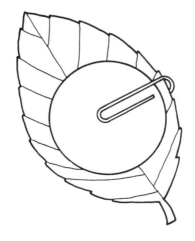

PLANTS NEED CORRECT AMOUNTS OF LIGHT.

Plants must have the right amount of sun to form the green food-making substance called chlorophyll. Experiment by clipping two circles of cardboard to the opposite sides of a growing green leaf. After three days remove the circles to see what happens when the light is shut off.

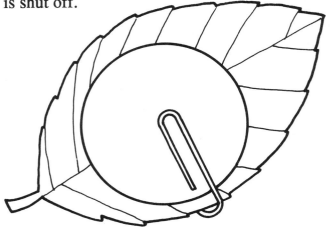

PLANTS NEED CORRECT AMOUNTS OF WATER.

Plants differ in the amounts of water they require. Experiment with three "flowering plants." Keep plant #1 slightly moist and water when it is dry one-half inch (1.27 cm) below the top of the soil. Clog up the drainage holes of #2. Water daily, allowing water to stand so the soil feels soggy. For plant #3 give absolutely no water at all.

PLANTS NEED THE CORRECT TEMPERATURE.

Plants adapt to a particular temperature range. Extremes in heat and cold will affect a plant's growth. Experiment by putting three plants in different temperatures—one in high heat, one in normal heat, and one in the freezer.

PLANTS NEED A GOOD SUPPLY OF OXYGEN.

Plants need good clean air! Smoke and smog affect plant growth, sometimes even killing the plant. Put one plant inside a plastic bag, push all the air out and tie the bag closed. In a second bag, have an adult release smoke into the bag and tie it.

Cycle of Nature

Information

Animals, humans, and plants are all linked together by a circular process we call the *Cycle of Nature*. This natural process runs on the energy of sunlight.

Plants use sunlight to create their own food in order to grow and, in the process, give off oxygen into the air. Man and animals breathe in the oxygen and eat the plants. They exhale carbon dioxide as a waste product of their body chemistry. Plants combine the carbon dioxide with water and minerals from the soil along with the energy from the sunlight to create more food to grow on. In the process, they give back oxygen into the air. When animals and plants die, they decay, and in the process return minerals to the soil where plants can soak them up again and the cycle of nature continues.

Project

Hypothesize whether reading to plants affects their growth. Conduct an experiment to prove or disprove it.

Directions

1. Discuss the exchange of oxygen with carbon dioxide during the breathing process.

2. Divide plants into two groups of three plants each. Place them in areas some distance apart, being sure that the plants all receive equal amounts of water, light, and heat. Use index cards to label the groups "Plants We Read To" and the other "Plants We Don't Read To."

3. Over a period of several weeks have students take turns reading to the first group of plants. Be sure the second group is some distance away.

4. Measure and record the growth of all six plants. At the end of several weeks draw your own conclusions. Write a brief statement to explain your experiment and to confirm or deny the hypothesis.

5. Discuss whether our bodies benefit from the increased oxygen and whether an increase in carbon dioxide benefited the plants.

Materials

- Six small established plants, all about the same size
- Sprayer bottle with water
- Ruler
- Paper
- Pencil
- Two index cards

Plant Kingdoms

Information

Botanists have studied the plant kingdom and categorized all plants into subkingdoms, grouping plants by similar characteristics. *Flowering plants* make up the largest group. *Cone-bearing plants,* also called conifers or evergreens, usually have needlelike or scalelike leaves. *Ferns* grow in moist wooded regions ranging from only a few feet in height to over 40 feet (12.2 m) in the tropics. *Club mosses* and *horsetails* were among the first plants to grow on land regions in prehistoric times. *Liverworts* and *mosses* grow in all parts of the world, usually in shady woodland places. *Algae* are simple plants that live mostly in water and damp areas. *Fungi,* most familiar as mushrooms, also grow in damp places. There are many varieties, some helpful and some harmful to mankind.

Project

Create a live plant display for each plant subkingdom.

Directions

1. Divide the class into seven groups. Assign each group a plant subkingdom, for which they are to gather information and set up a small plant display.

2. Create a backdrop on poster board to show an appropriate terrain for the plants.

3. Use index cards for titles and descriptive labels. Be sure to include the names of students who worked on the exhibit.

3. Connect the poster board pieces accordion-style and place the plants in front of their proper subkingdom.

Materials

- Plants supplied by the students
- Poster board
- Clear tape
- Colored marking pens
- Ruler
- Index cards
- Reference books

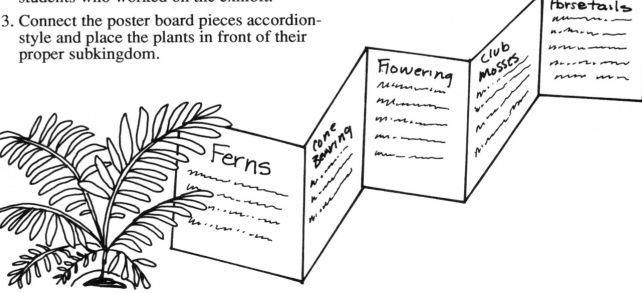

Plant Parts

Information

Plants live under a wide variety of conditions, evolving and adapting to their region's environment. They are found growing in almost every part of the world: in deserts, on high mountains and flat plains, in ponds, marshes, and oceans. There are plants in some parts of the polar regions.

Plants, like all other living things, are composed of cells which are put together in special ways to do special jobs. Together they become the many parts of a plant. Most plants have roots, stems or branches, and leaves, which make up the vegetative plant parts. The flowers, along with the fruits and seeds they produce, are the reproductive parts.

Project

Research and teach one plant-related topic through a diagram or drawing. Display diagrams and drawings on bulletin board.

Directions

1. Select a topic from the list below. Research and teach the topic with an oral report and a chart or drawing.

   - Plants and the Cycle of Nature
   - Where Plants Live (map)
   - Growth of a Green Plant
   - How a Seed Develops into a Plant
   - Parts of a Flowering Plant
   - Parts of a Root
   - Types of Root Systems
   - Parts of a Stem (Woody and Nonwoody)
   - Parts of a Leaf
   - Types of Leaves
   - Parts of a Flower (Outer Parts/Inner Parts)
   - Parts of a Seed
   - How Flowering Plants Reproduce
   - How Cone-Bearing Plants Reproduce
   - How Ferns Reproduce
   - How Plants Reproduce by Propagation
   - How Plants Grow Longer and Wider

Materials

- Reference books
- Poster board or card-weight paper
- Colored pencils
- Black, fine-point marker
- Ruler
- Pencil

Seeds of Flowering Plants

Information

Any plant that produces a seed, fruit, and flower is considered a *flowering plant*. This category includes brightly-colored garden plants that bloom, most vegetables, fruits, grains, herbs, wildflowers, grasses, water plants, cacti, trees, and shrubs. Most flowering plants have four main parts: *roots, stems, leaves,* and *flowers*. The reproductive parts are found in the flowers which produce the fruits which contain the seeds. The size of flowering plants varies considerably. The tiny floating duckweed is just one-fiftieth of an inch (.5 mm) long. Some flowering trees measure over 300 feet (91.4 m) tall.

Project

Make an egg-carton seed museum to determine if seed size relates to full-grown plant size.

Directions

1. Divide into small groups, each group selecting a category of flowering plants. Select seeds for 12 different plants in the chosen category.

2. Make a grid of two rows of six squares on the inside of the egg carton lid to correspond to the 12 sections in the carton.

3. Pour potting soil into the sections, filling to the top. Mist lightly with water.

4. Glue five or six seeds in a square on the lid, then plant five or six of the same seeds in the corresponding cup by poking six shallow holes, dropping the seeds in, and gently covering them.

5. Do this for each section, making sure the seeds at the top match the seeds planted in the corresponding hole.

6. Mist lightly and cover the soil-filled cups with plastic wrap. When sprouts begin pushing up, carefully cut slits in the plastic wrap for them to grow through while leaving the soil covered to conserve moisture.

7. Observe and draw your own conclusions: ***Does the size of the seed determine the size of the plant?***

Materials

- Variety of seed packets
- Cardboard egg cartons
- Potting soil
- Clear plastic wrap
- Spray mist bottle
- Water
- Glue
- Ruler
- Dark pencil or pen

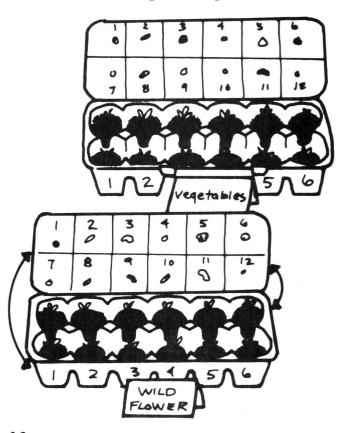

Seeds Travel

Information ༄ ༄ ༄ ༄ ༄ ༄ ༄ ༄ ༄ ༄ ༄ ༄ ༄ ༄

Many plants depend on the wind to move their seeds to new areas. Seeds of the milkweed, bullthistle, cattails, cottonwood, and dandelion plants sail on the gentlest breeze like tiny fluffy parachutes. Some seeds, like the maple and elm, have thin wing-like parts sticking out to catch the wind and glide through the air. Tumbleweeds scatter their seeds as they roll along the ground. Cockleburs, burdocks, and sticktights have stickers or hooks that snag onto our clothes or the fur of animals and fall off later in another place. Lupin seed pods dry out until they pop open, flinging their seeds outward. Some seeds like the lotus water lily and coconut fall into water and float to a new spot. People move seeds when they buy seed packets to plant in yards, gardens and indoor pots. No matter how seeds travel, they usually end up far away from their parent plant.

Project

Read seed packets and map the plants' geographic regions.

Materials

- Variety of plant seed packets
- Copies of the Plant Map, following
- Colored pencils

Directions

1. Collect a variety of seed packets.
2. After reading the backs of the packets, indicate by name and drawing on the Plant Map where each plant would grow best.
3. List the plants best suited for your area and use these seeds in your plant experiments.

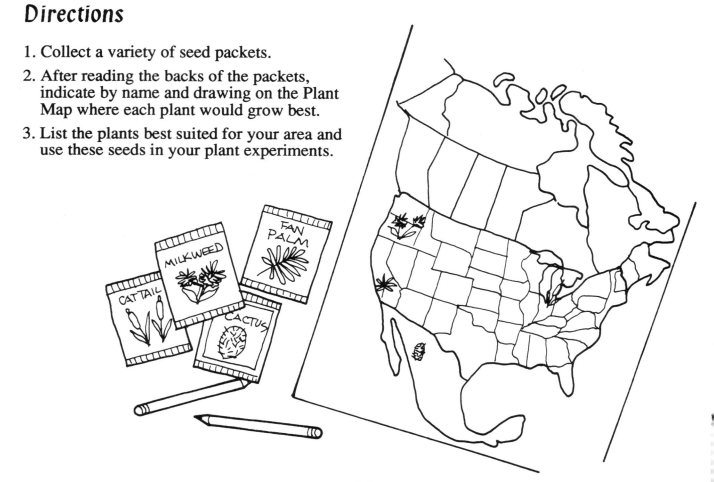

Stems

Information

Stems hold the leaves and flowers of a plant upright in the air so they can receive sunlight. Inside the stem are little tubes called *xylem* that carry water and food from the roots up to the leaves and thence to the other parts of the plant.

Some plants like vines, flowers, and grasses have soft stems. Trees and bushes have one hard woody trunk and smaller branches and twigs, all of which are stems. The stems of the strawberry plant grow along the ground, starting new root systems. Many common flowers sprout from the underground stems of rootlike *bulbs, corms, rhizomes,* or *tubers.* White potato stems grow underground. Lettuce and cabbage have large leaves but such short stems it appears they have none at all.

Project

Conduct or observe experiments to learn how water is conducted up through the xylem in plant stems.

Directions

1. Divide into small groups. Conduct the two experiments on the following page.
2. Write about the experiments in the Botanist's Journal (page 6), telling what you observed and why you think you got the results you did.

Materials

- Celery stalks
- One long-stemmed white carnation
- Clear plastic glasses
- Modeling clay
- Water
- Measuring cup
- Red and blue food coloring
- Paper
- Pencil
- Stem Experiments page, following
- Botanist's Journal, page 6

1. Water Pressure

Plants that are full of water stand erect and if bent, will return to their upright position. What happens to plant cells when a plant is deprived of water? Why?

Materials

- Two glasses
- Two wilted celery stalks
- Blue food coloring
- Modeling clay
- Botanist's Journal, page 6
- Pencil
- Crayons or colored pencils

Directions

1. Fill two glasses half-full of water. Add blue food coloring until the water is dark blue.

2. Cut a slice from one celery stalk so water can rise up the tubes.

3. Plug the bottom of the other celery stalk with clay so no water can rise up the tubes.

4. Let the celery stand for 24 hours.

5. Draw an illustration of what happened and explain why in the Botanist's Journal.

2. Moisture & Minerals

Minerals in the soil are important to plant growth and development. How are minerals transported up the stem to reach the leaves and flowers?

Materials

- Measuring cup
- Two glasses
- Long-stemmed white carnation
- Red and blue food coloring
- Botanist's Journal, page 6
- Pencil
- Crayons or colored pencils

Directions

1. Pour ½ cup (118 ml) of water in each glass. Add red food coloring to one glass and blue food coloring to the other until the water is colored darkly.

2. Cut the lower half of the carnation stem in half lengthwise.

3. Put one half in red water, the other in blue water.

4. Let it stand 48 hours.

5. Draw an illustration of what happened and explain why in the Botanist's Journal.

Roots

Information

Roots grow mostly under the ground, anchoring the plant and absorbing the water and minerals that the plant needs to grow from the soil. For some plants like carrots, beets, radishes, jicama, and potatoes, the roots also store food for the plant. Root systems can be *fibrous* or *taproot*. Fibrous roots, like those of grasses, have many same-sized slender roots that grow out in all directions from the plant. A taproot plant has one large root that grows straight down, some down to 15 feet (4.6 m) or more into the soil. From a plant's seed a primary root develops producing smaller secondary roots and root hairs which greatly increase the plant's ability to absorb water and minerals from the soil.

Project

Have a root-tasting party and chart the class favorites.

Directions

1. Examine and discuss the appearance and other qualities of the root vegetables.

2. Divide into small groups to prepare the root vegetables and the dip for tasting (with adult supervision).

3. While tasting, talk about what you like and dislike about colors, textures, tastes, etc. and different ways your parents prepare them at home. Chart everyone's favorite root vegetable on poster board and leave the chart on display.

Materials

- Variety of root vegetables (carrots, radishes, jicama, turnips, beets, potatoes, sweet potatoes)
- Packaged vegetable dip mix
- Ingredients required for mixing with dip (see package directions)
- Slicer/peeler
- Paper serving plates
- Paper napkins
- Paring knife
- Poster board
- Marking pens

Grasses

Information

Grasses are one of the largest and most varied plant kingdoms, growing on almost every land surface on Earth. They range from short lawn grasses to tall woody bamboo canes. The cereal grasses such as corn, oats, wheat, and barley are used to make breakfast cereals, breads, alcoholic beverages, pastes, paper, and plastics. A grass plant called sugar cane supplies most of the sugar we eat. Grasses beautify lawns, playgrounds, and parks. Grass roots prevent *erosion* (wearing away) of fertile topsoil by wind and rain.

Project

Turn a blade of grass into a simple reed instrument.

Materials

• Large blade of grass

Directions

1. Hold the blade of grass between your thumbs and the heels of your hands.

2. Blow hard over the edge of the grass blade between your thumbs.

3. Why does the grass make a loud squawking sound?

4. Can you play a tune with the grass reed?

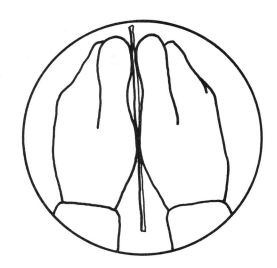

Bamboo

Information

Bamboo is a giant grass that can grow up to 120 feet (37 m) high and have stems up to one foot (30 cm) in diameter. It is distantly related to wheat, oats, and barley, and grows in tropical or temperate climates.

There are many uses for bamboo. In the United States it is used mostly for ornaments. In other areas of the world bamboo is used in making houses, furniture, sandals, fences, animal pens, baskets, and cooking utensils, among other items. Young bamboo sprouts are eaten as a vegetable.

Project

Make and play a bamboo panpipe.

Materials

- Bamboo pieces (obtained at plant nurseries or lumber yards)
- Modeling clay
- Clear tape
- Scissors

Directions

1. Cut the bamboo into varied lengths from two to eight inches (5 cm to 20 cm).

2. Seal one end of each piece with clay.

3. Tape the pieces together from smallest to longest with top open ends level.

4. Play the panpipe by placing the open end against the lower lip and blowing very gently across the top edges.

5. How does the pitch change when you blow across them?

6. Practice until you can play some tunes.

 # Wacky Plant Names

Using the list of Wacky Plant Names, create a word search on the grid below.
Just for fun, research to find wacky plant names on your own!

Baby's Breath
Bachelor's Buttons
Black-Eyed Susan
Blazing Star
Bleeding Heart
Bloodroot
Bluebonnet
Butter and Eggs
Buttercup
Butterprint Shakers
Cowslip
Dandelion
Devil's Paintbrush

Dogtooth Violet
Dog Wood
Dutchman's Britches
Fireweed
Forget-Me-Not
Four O'Clock
Foxtails
Goldenrod
Horse Nettles
Indian Paintbrush
Jack-in-the-Pulpit
Lady's Slippers
Lamb's Quarter

Oxeye Daisy
Quack Grass
Queen Anne's Lace
Shepherd's Purse
Shooting Star
Smartweed
Snapdragon
Soap Plant
St. John's Wort
Sweet William
Telegraph Plant
Touch-Me-Not
Witch Grass

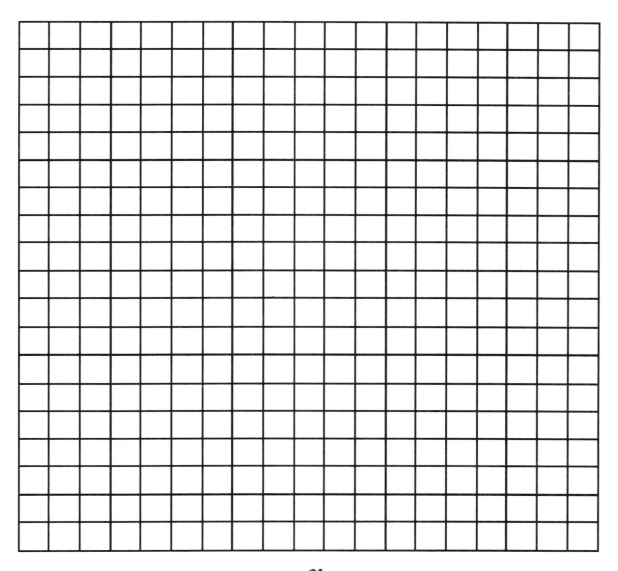

Flowers

Information

Flowers are the part of the plant that makes the seeds. A flower is made up of the *petals*, the *anther*, the *stigma*, and the *ovary*. But the tiny grains of *pollen* are the most important part of the seed-making process. Pollen is made in the anther, the male part of a flower. *Pollination* is when the right kinds of pollen get rubbed on to the *stigma*, the female part of a flower. Many plants pollinate themselves, counting on bees or winds to move the pollen from the anther to the stigma. But stronger, healthier seeds develop when the pollen comes from another plant of the same kind. When pollination has occurred, the ovary begins making the seeds.

Consider the importance of pollen: without pollen there would be no seeds. Without seeds, there would be no plants. Without plants there would be no foods. Without foods, there would be no animals or people.

Project

Closely examine and draw a diagram of a lily blossom. Label each part with a brief phrase describing its importance.

Materials

- One live lily blossom per group
- Copies of the Lily Diagram, following
- Pencils
- Paper towel

Directions

1. Divide into small groups. Duplicate the lily blossom page, one copy per group.

2. Working on a paper towel, examine the lily blossom carefully. Identify the plant parts. Discuss and take notes about what you deserve.

3. Diagram the flower, labeling and describing the purpose of each part.

4. Include a summary paragraph describing your work.

5. Share your projects and put them on display.

 # Flower Activities

In small groups, examine a variety of flower petals. For each, write descriptive words and phrases about how the petals look, feel, and smell. Measure their length and width. Try to determine what flower they are from.

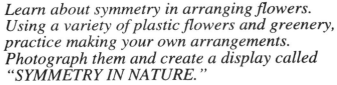

Bring in a single live flower in a small vase to observe carefully and sketch as a still life picture. Mount your picture and display.

Learn about symmetry in arranging flowers. Using a variety of plastic flowers and greenery, practice making your own arrangements. Photograph them and create a display called "SYMMETRY IN NATURE."

Petal Mystery

Information

Water and nutrients needed by a plant are usually absorbed by the plant's roots through a process called osmosis. The materials absorbed are carried up through the plant through the tube-like xylem in a process called capillary action.

The same kind of process can be seen when you use a cloth to absorb spilled water from a table: the liquid moves up through tiny "tubes" in the fibers of the cloth, lifting it upward from the surface. It is the presence of water in the parts of a plant that help keep it standing upright.

Project

Learn about capillary action that provides moisture and nutrients in a plant by observing the opening of a paper flower.

Directions

1. Color the flower shape as you choose. Cut it out on the dark lines and fold inward on the broken lines like an unopened blossom.

2. Fill bowl with water to one inch (2.5 cm) from the top. Float your closed blossom on the water and tell why you think the petals are slowly opening.

3. How is this similar to the way a plant receives water and nutrients?

Materials

- Smooth paper (no gloss)
- Copies of flower shape below
- Colored pencils
- Bowl
- Water
- Scissors

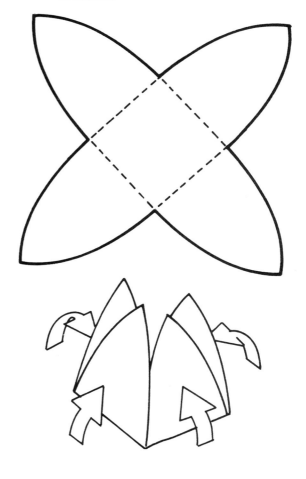

Fruits

Information

To botanists all seed-bearing plants, including vegetables and fruits, bear fruit. Crops listed as *fruits* usually grow on fleshy-stemmed plants, vines, shrubs, or trees that live and grow to produce fruit for many years. Tomatoes and melons are properly called *vegetable fruit* because they develop from seeds and grow for a single season.

Fruits are classified as *tropical, subtropical,* and *temperate fruits.* Hundreds of tropical fruits are grown and eaten by people living in tropical regions, but bananas, pineapple, coconut, mango, guava, papaya, and kiwi are the ones most commonly shipped to other countries. Subtropical fruits include citrus (oranges, grapefruit, tangerines, lemons and limes), olives, figs, dates, and avocados. Temperate fruits are apples, grapes, berries, peaches, pears, plums, apricots, cherries, pomegranates, persimmons, and nuts.

Project

Examine seed placement in fruit by slicing and drawing vertical and horizontal cross-sections.

Directions

1. Have an adult available to cut the fruits into vertical and horizontal cross-sections.

2. Divide into small groups, each group choosing a fruit. Observe the cut fruit and make a sketch in the Botanist's Journal of the seed placement.

3. Label the sketch.

4. Put the fruit on paper plates for sampling.

Materials

- Apples, pears, peaches, cherries, grapes, citrus, berries, and nuts
- Slicing knife (used only by an adult)
- Paper plates
- Paper
- Pencil
- Botanist's Journal, page 6

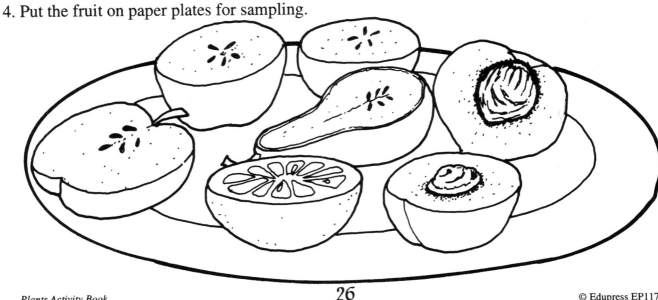

Pollen Carriers

Information

How does pollen get from one flower to another? The most obvious way is the wind. But most plants count on animals to carry their pollen. As a tiny animal flits from flower to flower looking for sweet nectar or tiny insects to eat, it brushes against the anthers and is soon covered with the sticky grains of pollen. As it visits other blossoms, some of the pollen rubs off on the stigmas. When the pollen ends up on the same kind of plants, *pollination* occurs.

Bees do most of the work of pollination. But so do birds, bugs and bats. Other small mammals like rats, mice, and possums brush against the pollen while slurping nectar from the blossoms. Some scientists believe the giraffe even pollinates the tree blossoms it leaves uneaten. Just imagine what one gigantic, long-necked sneeze could do for those trees!

Project

Show how pollen is carried by playing the "Birds, Bees, and Flowers" game, using glitter for pollen.

Directions

1. Divide into three groups, designating a group #1, group #2, and group #3.

2. Groups #2 and #3 pair off, holding up their hands London Bridge-style as flowers. Give each pair one small jar of pollen glitter to sprinkle on the visiting animals.

3. Group #1 are pollen-carriers who must hurry to a new flower each time the whistle blows. At each flower they will get a little "pollen," wait and listen for the whistle, then move quickly to a different flower. Only one animal at a time can go into each flower. (Have one extra person left out in the open to add excitement.)

4. After several times, students change places. Rotation continues until every group has had a turn at each role.

5. At the game's end each child should show the different colors of pollen they collected and carried to other flowers.

Materials

- Small jars of glitter in various colors (only a few holes open to limit amount of glitter)
- Whistle
- Grassy area

Leafy Food Factories

Information

The job of leaves is to create food for a plant from carbon dioxide, light, water and minerals. The food is stored in the roots, stems, seeds, and fruits to provide continuous energy for all of the parts of the plant to grow and flourish. Although a leaf appears to be flat, under a microscope one can see there is a space between the upper and lower skin covering. In this tiny space the "factory" works to change water and carbon dioxide into sugars when light and chlorophyll (a green substance) are present. Air coming in through pores on the underside of the leaf and light striking the top of the leaf flood the cells inside to make chlorophyll. In many deciduous leaves, the stronger the light, the more sugar is produced. But many evergreens and tiny shrubs and herbs that live on the forest floor make food in very little light.

Project

Walk, collect leaves, measure, make rubbings, and mount them, designating them as either deciduous or evergreen.

Materials

- Plastic or paper bags
- Construction paper
- Pencil
- Crayons
- Glue
- Ruler

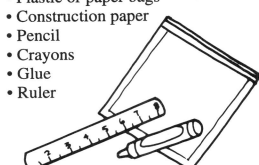

Directions

1. Take a walking tour of the neighborhood to collect a wide variety of leaves in a plastic or paper bag.

2. Measure the length of the leaves and stems.

3. Examine leaves to discover the purpose of their veins. Discuss findings. Make leaf rubbings of some of the leaves.

4. Divide a large sheet of construction paper in half, marking one column **Deciduous** and the other column **Evergreen**.

5. Categorize the leaves by gluing them under the correct column.

6. Put the mounted leaf collections on display.

Poisonous Plants

Information

There are about 700 kinds of poisonous plants growing in the United States and Canada. Many of them look, smell, or taste disagreeable, so animals and humans leave them alone. But many, like mushrooms, look very similar to plants that are eaten every day. It is important not to eat any part of a plant that is unfamiliar to you.

There are some plants that do not have to be eaten to cause harm. Poison ivy, poison oak, and poison sumac are plants that cause irritation in your eyes or on your skin. The leaves of these plants contain a gummy oil that will rub off on the skin or clothing of anyone brushing against the plant. The poison serves as a protection for the plant against animals. The appearance of these plants can confuse us. They can be compact bushes or long trailing vines. The leaves vary in size, but always grow in threes with one leaf on top and one on each side. The color of the leaves will change season to season.

The best thing to do about these poisonous plants is to avoid them. When walking in wooded areas, always wear long-legged, long-sleeved clothing to keep from getting the itchy blisters. Since they won't show up for a day or two, it's a good idea to wash yourself and your clothes, including shoes, with soap and water as soon as possible.

Project

Create posters showing sinister plots and faces on a poison ivy or other poisonous plant. Add a couplet or caption to describe the plant or offer a warning against it.

Materials

- Reference books
- Colored pencils
- Paper
- Pencil

Directions

1. Divide into groups, each group choosing a poisonous plant from the list.

2. Create a poster about your chosen plant. Include important information and warnings in bold print.

3. Share your poster and put it on display in the classroom.

All or some parts of these plants are poisonous:

- Monkshood
- Chinaberry
- Gelsemium
- Mountain laurel
- Oleander
- Rhubarb (leaves)

- Azalea
- Daphne
- Jimson weed
- Poisonous mushrooms
- Poison hemlock
- Tobacco (leaves)

- Belladonna
- Foxglove
- Mistletoe (berries)
- Nightshade
- Rhododendron

Carnivorous Plants

Information

Carnivorous plants are meat-eating plants—that is, plants that eat insects. They can thrive in nutrient-poor habitats that lack an adequate mineral supply. These unusual plants have special organs that enable them to trap and digest insects in their own leaves, thus obtaining the needed minerals. They also make their own food by photosynthesis. Some examples of insect-eating plants are the Venus's flytrap, the butterwort, the sundew, the pitcher plant, and the monkey's drinking cup. Contrary to primitive folk-tales, carnivorous plants do not eat small pets or children.

The Venus's flytrap grows in the boggy coastal regions of North and South Carolina. It grows to be about one foot (30 cm) tall, and has white blossoms and oddly-shaped leaves. The leaves are made up of two parts—a lower bladelike section and an upper half with two lobes hinged to a lid. Each lobe has three sensitive hairs on its surface and is edged with a fringe of sharp bristles. When an insect touches one of the hairs, the lobes close and hold the insect inside. The soft parts of the insect are digested by a special fluid secreted by glands in the leaf.

Project

- Observe a Venus's flytrap to see it eat.
- Create a pictorial display of other carnivorous plants.

Directions

1. Obtain a Venus's flytrap and place it at a station in the room where it can be easily observed throughout the day. Observe its eating activity as the opportunity arises.

2. Make notes about your observations in the Botanist's Journal.

3. Use resource books to find pictures of other carnivorous plants.

4. Use your choice of art media to duplicate the pictures.

5. Arrange a display of carnivorous plant pictures near the Venus's flytrap.

Materials

- Venus's flytrap, available at plant nurseries
- Botanist's Journal (page 6)
- Resource books on plants
- Paper
- Art media of choice
- Supply of live flies (see mail-order source below)

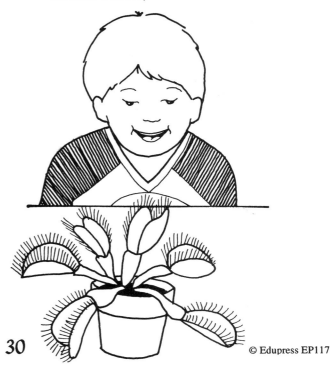

> **Mail-Order Source:**
> Insect Lore Products
> Nature Kits
> Box 1535
> Shafter CA 93263
> 1-800-LIVE BUG

Gardening

Information

Home gardening can be enjoyed by anyone who wants pleasant recreation, an absorbing hobby, an herb or medicine garden, a fresh supply of fruits and vegetables, or the beauty of flowers in and around their home.

There are rock gardens, shaded courtyard/patio gardens in hot dry regions, roof gardens atop tall buildings, water gardens with pools, streams and water plants, mathematically exact formal gardens on large estates, sweeping flower borders edging green lawns and sidewalks, patches of bright wildflowers surrounding a country home, and square-foot gardens in one corner of the school playground.

Gardeners have many tasks in looking after their plants—finding the best spot and time of year for planting, enriching the soil, raking and leveling the surface, planting weed-free seeds, keeping them fed, stirred, watered, and weeded, protecting them from high winds, insects, animals, and diseases. People of all ages can be successful home gardeners.

Project

Plant various types of square-foot gardens.

Materials

- Plants planned and gathered by students
- Plastic planting containers
- Potting soil
- Watering/misting container
- Water

Directions

1. Divide into small groups, each group selecting one variety of garden listed in the information above or creating their own.

2. Working in approximately one square foot (30.5 cm square) of space, plan, plant and care for your garden, keeping notes for a later presentation.

3. Six to eight weeks later present your garden and relate your experience, your problems and successes, and what you learned from the project. Display the gardens with labels and brief written explanations.

Woodlands

Information

Finding woodland areas for exploring and collecting samples of nature can be tricky. City or state parks that contain wooded areas are probably best for younger city children. Avoid nature preserves and bird sanctuaries which protect wild living things and do not allow for taking anything out. Strict laws impose fines or worse for those removing any specimens. Designated wilderness areas are good but can be hard to find.

Care must be taken in removing woodland litter in order to disturb the area as little as possible. Remember that each area is the *habitat* or home of many tiny woodland creatures and you are the intruder. Respect it in the way that you would want your home respected.

Project

Take a field trip to a wooded area to gather specimens.

Materials

- Camera
- Comfortable walking shoes
- Long-legged and long-sleeved clothing
- Lightweight gloves
- Sunscreen
- Insect repellent
- Small hand shovels
- Large plastic bags with zip closures
- Small spray bottle of water
- Large shoe box
- Small shovels

Directions

1. Find a small heavily wooded area appropriate for digging and collecting (not a designated nature sanctuary or preserve). Get permission to explore and bring out a few specimens. Choose a warm day, preferably after a rain. Keep the time spent walking as short as possible.

2. Upon arrival sit down, observe, draw, and take notes about the appearance of the terrain and what is immediately over, around, and under you.

3. Choose a spot with abundant "mulchy litter" under the trees. Using shovels instead of hands, carefully lift up an area about six inches (15.2 cm) square and four inches (10.2 cm) deep and put it in a plastic bag. If it seems dry, spray with a *tiny amount* of water before sealing the bag.

4. Take specimens back to class to continue examining them with Mulchy Litter activities, following.

Mulchy Litter

Information

Mulchy litter is that deep layer of decaying grass and leaves, bits of rotting wood, tree seedlings, minute lichen-laden rocks, small insects, tiny ferns or violet plants, mushrooms and other organisms found beneath a tree. A *naturalist*, or one who studies nature, can learn a great deal from examining the shape, texture, dimensions, size, and colors of the miniature colony that dwells under the broad leafy canopy. They are careful not to disturb the area unnecessarily. They always try to get the roots of any plants they dig up. They carefully place inanimate objects into cardboard boxes and live specimens in misted plastic bags. They take everything back to their laboratory in order to compare, contrast, and classify their findings into categories; to count, graph, diagram, and to record their observations in a journal or notebook. They often share new information with other scientists and set up displays in nature museums for public viewing.

Project

Examine mulchy litter; count and categorize specimens, then mount and display them.

Directions

1. Work outdoors. Trap and remove any moving creatures and keep like kinds in tiny jars. Poke pinholes in the lids. Spiders will appreciate a twig to spin their webs on.

2. Work on a double layer of newspaper. Be sure litter is moist. Gently pour out the litter in a centered mound. Be prepared to catch any live critters you missed in step #1.

3. Using sticks instead of fingers, carefully spread the litter into a thin layer. Begin by setting the larger pieces of material out to the side, grouping things into categories. Examine the material slowly, discussing observations, similarities, body parts, and coverings, size, and quantity. Use a magnifying glass and small ruler.

4. When finished, mount and label specimens for display. Return leftover litter to the plastic bag, mist well with water, seal and store in a dark, cool place to use in the self-contained garden project on page 34.

Materials

- Sheets of newspaper
- Plastic bags of collected litter (see previous page)
- Several baby food jars
- Throw-away sticks for probes
- Tweezers
- Small rulers marked in both inches and centimeters
- Measuring cups
- Scissor
- Disinfectant soap
- Small spray bottle of water
- Cardboard for mounting
- Glue

Controlling Pests

Information

Mother Nature provides gardeners with a wealth of creatures that love to eat plant-chewing and sucking pests. Ladybugs and praying mantises eat "bad" insects and do not harm plants. Feeding stations attract insect-eating birds like the flycatcher which catch insects in flight. Stones in cool corners attract frogs, toads, lizards, and non-poisonous snakes. Gardeners observe droppings, tweeze and squash worms, toss snails and slugs in saltwater, use cardboard collars for cutworms, cut around tiny holes in leaves, snip off the yellow, egg-laden or damaged leaves, scratch around the soil for buried plant-eating worms, wash away droppings with a spray of water, and place diseased plants in the trash. They discourage larger animals like rabbits with an 18-inch (45.7-cm) chicken-wire fence. Gardeners who are attentive to their plants' needs will harvest bountifully and enjoy the fruits of their labors.

Project

Make a miniature self-contained garden to observe and practice good plant care and pest control.

Materials

- Collected woodland litter from field trip
- A leaky aquarium with a glass cover
- Activated charcoal from pet store
- Package of potting soil
- Spray bottle with water
- Small frog or toad
- Small crickets
- Tiny plant pests
- Gravel
- Tree seedlings
- Small lizard
- Small snails
- Magnifying glass
- Tweezers
- Plants

Directions

1. Place the empty aquarium in an area of filtered or indirect sunlight and an even temperature. Decide whether the garden will be seen from all sides or against a wall.

2. Spread a 1½-inch (3.8-cm) layer of gravel in the aquarium.

3. Add a one-inch (2.54-cm) layer of a mixture of charcoal and gravel (to keep the soil from souring).

4. Follow with a three-inch (7.6-cm) layer of potting soil, creating interesting hills and depressions.

5. Cover with a half-inch (1.27-cm) layer of organic material collected on the Woodland Walk (page 33).

6. Plant the largest plants and tree seedlings near the back if against a wall, otherwise near the center. Allowing plenty of room for growth, add smaller plants, rocks, branches.

7. Add little creatures and pests collected on the walk.

8. Arrange top soil naturally. Water until moisture appears in the lowest level. Mist the plants daily and keep covered.

9. Care for the plants as suggested above. Keep journal notes on care given to plants, observations of problems and pest control.

Plant Diseases

Information ꙮꙮꙮꙮꙮꙮꙮꙮꙮꙮꙮꙮꙮꙮ

World-wide there are 80,000 known plant diseases. All plants are susceptible to one or more of them. The most common cause of poor plant health is low levels of soil minerals (nitrogen, phosphorus, and iron) which causes yellow or deformed leaves. Too much water causes rotting. Pesticides and pollutants in the air (ozone from spray cans, and sulfur dioxide and nitrous oxide from smoke and car exhaust) dissolve in rain water and fall to the earth as acid rain, causing crops and forests to become diseased and die. Lightning, freezing, foliage-eating animals or insects, and farm machinery can all create wounds that invite infectious disease, such as a virus, fungus (rust, smut, and mildew), parasitic plants (mistletoe), and microscopic worms.

Crop rotation can replace a diseased crop, but the best disease control is simply keeping the agent causing the problem away from the plants. On a small scale, just pruning the diseased part off the plant helps. On a larger scale there are laws restricting the importing of problematic plants and fruits. Although scientists continually work to develop disease-resistant plants, there are disease organisms constantly evolving to infect the plant world.

Project

Hold a Plant Clinic Day to teach students about plants, as well as to diagnose and write prescriptions for sick plants brought in by students.

Directions

1. Invite a botanist or local nursery employee to be a guest "plant doctor" for Plant Clinic Day. Discuss with them the props and white doctor's coat. Print up "prescription sheets " with a large Rx at the top. (Call to confirm a day or two before.)

2. Announce "Plant Clinic Day." Invite parents to help students find sick leaves and wounded, diseased, deformed, or pest-infested plants. Ask that plants be packaged in a plastic bag labeled with the plant name (if known) and student's name. Have them bring plant-patients on Plant Clinic Day and send them home the same day so students can begin journaling their "treatment."

3. Set aside a day when students share their Journal and their recovered plant.

Materials

- "Plant Clinic Day " notice
- Prescription sheets
- White lab coat
- Doctor props
- Plastic bags with ties
- Folded sheets of paper for a "Before and After Plant Journal of Treatment"
- Ruler for measuring growth

Weeds

Information

A gardener's worst enemy is not the weather or pests or diseases. It is that fast-growing sun/water/nutrient-stealer–the common weed. Any plant growing where it is not wanted is considered a weed. Weeds crowd out good plants, block sunlight, soak up nutrients, cling to other plants and weigh them down, sometimes killing them. But weeds hold the soil in heavy rains.

Animals and people dislike weeds that bring on hay fever (ragweed), cause serious itchy rashes (poison oak and poison ivy), cling to fur or clothing (nettles), and get deep into animals' ears (foxtails).

Project

Observe dandelion seeds blowing; hand-weed them, bag them, measure the root lengths, and eat the leaves in a green salad.

Materials

- Plastic bags
- Spray bottle
- Water
- Rulers (inches/centimeters)
- Chart paper
- Pencil

Directions

1. Get permission to use an area full of dandelions.

2. Sit quietly and observe the wind blowing the white seed heads. Pick a few heads and blow the seeds.

2. In pairs, practice using the correct way to pull dandelions. Their roots can grow to three feet (.9 m) deep so a gentle persistent tug is best. The goal is to extract the whole root. Save them.

3. Place dandelion plants in a plastic bag and mist lightly. Seal the bag to take back to class.

4. Handling the plants carefully, measure the roots, chart the sizes, and figure the average size. Then present the record-holders for the longest roots, leaves and total plant.

5. Rebag and refrigerate the dandelion plants to be washed and used in a green salad.

Propagation

Information

Propagation occurs when part of one plant grows into a complete new plant. All parts of the plant—the root, stem, leaf, or flower— can be propagated. Some plants propagate through new shoots from an underground stem. The most common form of propagation can be seen in strawberry plants which send out *runners* that take root and grow into new plants. Many berries, ferns, irises, and grasses propagate from such "running stems."

Gardeners and farmers use *cutting, grafting, and layering* to create new plants. To increase potato crops, farmers cut potatoes into sections containing one *eye* (bud), each of which will become a new potato plant. Grafting involves cuttings (upper part of a plant) that are attached to the *stock* or lower part (root and stem) of another plant. *Mound layering* is soil mounded up around the base of a plant causing the branches to grow roots. In *air layering* a three-inch (7.6-cm) cut is made halfway through a branch then surrounded with sphagnum moss and wrapped to make it waterproof. When new roots grow in the moss, the branch is cut and planted. The result of careful propagation is a new plant that will have the desired characteristics to improve the species.

Project

Observe the growth of a sweet potato plant in a propagation method similar to cutting.

Directions

1. Select a sweet potato that has several "eyes."

2. Stick several toothpicks around the circumference of the sweet potato.

3. Fill the jar with water about three-quarters full.

4. Put one end of the potato into the water, resting the toothpicks on the lip of the jar to keep the potato suspended in the water.

5. Add water to the jar daily as it is used or evaporated.

6. Observe what changes take place in the "eyes" that are below the water level.

Materials

• Sweet potato
• Glass jar with wide neck
• Toothpicks

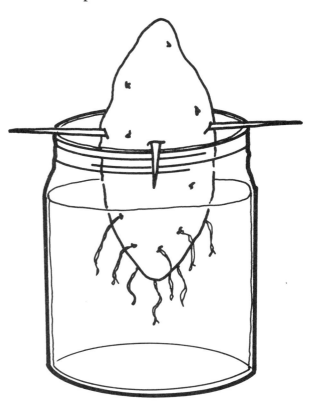

Propagation

Rooting new plants from old is a simple matter. Cut a branch off then take cuttings from it. The new tips of the plant are called the soft wood, the middle half-ripened part is medium wood. If the lower, thickest part looks woody, it is called the hard wood. Summer cuttings of medium wood will root best.

Project

Plant cuttings (slips) from selected plants.

Materials

- House plant
- Scissors
- Green Light Rootone® or potting soil
- Pencil
- Wide dish or pot for planting

Directions

1. Make several cuttings from the house plant. Choose only healthy, vigorously-growing plants for your new slips. Use the tips from branches that break off easily. For most house plants, cut tips about two to six inches (5 to 15 cm) long. Make an angled cut below a stem notch in the medium wood section so you have about two to three inches (5 to 7.5 cm) to plant under the soil. Remove all but three or four of the newest leaves and any buds and flowers.

2. Mark two inches (5 cm) on a pencil.

3. Fill the wide dish or pot with soil or Rootone®. Using the marked end of the pencil, make a hole for each of the cuttings, pushing the pencil down into the soil to the mark on the pencil.

4. Carefully put a cutting into each hole, carefully tamping soil down around the cutting.

5. Water the plant cuttings carefully, watching for new growth on the cuttings. After several weeks, gently pull one of the cuttings from the pot to examine the new root system.

Trees

Information

Trees are important for many reasons. They provide fruits and nuts to eat and many medicines. They cool and circulate the air and protect us from the sun's heat and harmful ultraviolet rays. They filter out smog and produce oxygen for animals and humans to breathe. They become barriers to block the winds of storms and the noises of busy highways. They stop erosion by breaking the heavy rainfall and by holding the soil with their roots. They produce many natural resources like wood, paper, and rubber. They add beauty and tranquility to our lives. They are home for many birds, insects, and other tree-dwelling creatures.

Project

- Create an exhibit or mural to illustrate the importance of trees.

Materials

- Resource books
- Materials as needed for each project
- Project page, following

Directions

1. Divide into three groups. Review the project page and assign a project to each group.
2. Brainstorm a list of materials needed for the individual projects.
3. Upon completion of the projects, present the information to the rest of the class.

Importance of Trees

Project

After discussing the information below, create an exhibit entitled *The Importance of Trees to Mankind.*

Wood Products
- Lumber is used for construction of homes and businesses.
- Lumber is used for everything from home and office furniture to recreational equipment, from boats to bridges.
- Lumber is broken down in one process that changes wood into paper, in another that changes wood pulp into alcohol and plastics.

Chemical Products
- Trees provide chemical ingredients needed for:

medicines	rubber
cosmetics	perfumes
paints	plastics
solvents	fertilizers

Food Products
- Trees provide food for the world's people:

fruits	maple syrup
nuts	chocolate
olives	coffee
spices	tea

Project

After discussing the information below, create a mural entitled *The Importance of Trees in Conserving Natural Resources.*

Conservation Aid
- Tree roots help to hold topsoil from washing away in heavy rainstorms.
- Tree roots help store ground water.
- Trees help prevent snowslides.
- Trees provide shelter for wildlife.
- Trees enhance recreation areas for vacationers and provide fuel for campfires.

Help for the Atmosphere
- Trees cool and circulate the air.
- Trees filter the harmful gases, like smog, in the atmosphere.
- Trees' leaves absorb carbon dioxide from the air while producing and releasing oxygen into the air.
- Trees protect us from the sun's heat and harmful ultraviolet rays.

Wind and Sound Breaks
- Trees planted as windbreaks in open country hold topsoil during storms.
- Trees planted as sound barriers help to block the noise of a busy highway.
- Trees planted as a rainfall break prevent erosion.

Project

Conduct demonstrations to show how trees are effective as wind and rainfall breaks.

- Use a sprinkler can of water and an evergreen branch to demonstrate how trees act as a rainfall break.
- Use an electric fan, an evergreen branch, and a piece of paper to demonstrate how trees act as a windbreak.

Tree Trunks

Information

The trunks of evergreen and deciduous trees are made up of four distinct layers wrapped in concentric circles around one another. A tree's hard, dead skin is called *cork* or *outer bark*. The purpose of bark is to protect the tree from injury, fungus, insects, forest fires and drought. It stretches, cracks, and dries, becoming grooved and rough, to allow the trunk and branches to grow. The *inner bark* called *phloem* is a layer of soft tissue that carries food made by the leaf "factories" to other parts of the tree through tiny pipelines. The *cambium* is a thin layer of growing tissue that keeps the roots, trunk, and branches growing thicker. The *xylem* is the woody center section of the trunk. Its *sapwood* on the outer part carries water and dissolved minerals *(sap)* from the roots to the leaves through tiny pipelines. The sturdy *heartwood* on the inner part helps to support the tree.

Most trees that grow where there are four definite seasons have two rings each year—a light-colored wider spring ring and a dark narrower summer ring. The size of the rings varies based on the amount of sunlight and moisture received. When the tree is cut down, we can count the number of ring pairs, called *annual rings*, seen on the cut surface and figure how old the tree is (35 ring pairs means 35 years old.) Black scars indicate fire damage. Cracks were caused by drying. "V" marks show where a branch once grew. Wider rings on only one side indicate the tree was slightly bent, requiring more wood to keep it from falling.

Project

Examine a slice of tree trunk, determine its age and diagram what you observe.

Directions

1. Divide the class into small groups. Call a tree-trimming company to request trunk samples for your project.

2. Examine the slice of tree trunk. Diagram it, labeling the layers. Add any markings you observe.

3. Write a brief paragraph explaining what you learned about the tree, telling its age and its life history as revealed in the rings and markings.

4. Share and display your tree diagram and history with the other groups.

Materials

- A two-inch (5 cm) slice of a tree trunk for each group
- Paper
- Colored pencils
- Pencil

Lost? Hug-A-Tree!

Information

A group of people in San Diego, California searched their local mountains for a nine-year-old boy who had gotten lost. The little boy later died because he kept wandering farther away instead of staying in the same spot, waiting to be found. His mother helped to develop an assembly program called "HUG-A-TREE AND SURVIVE" for schools and youth organizations. Their local Sheriff's Departments schedule and present this program that teaches children how to keep from getting lost. But if they should get lost, it also teaches them how to stay safe, comfortable, and **in the same spot** until they are found by simply hugging a tree.

For information and handouts send a stamped, self-addressed envelope to the National Office of HUG-A-TREE, PO Box 712739, Santee, CA 92072. Below is a recap of their assembly program, **printed with their permission.**

Project

Conduct a safety-awareness assembly program for your class, and footprint each child.

Directions

1. Get permission from your principal before beginning this project.

2. Learn the essential elements of the HUG-A-TREE program. Prepare and conduct your own version of this assembly program to present the information to others in your grade level or school.

3. Divide the class into small groups of two or three students. Assign groups to prepare to present the seven points directed to children and the four points directed to parents.

4. Brainstorm ways to demonstrate or role-play each point with props or action. Practice reading and role-playing your parts.

5. After several "dress rehearsals" schedule a presentation for other classes. Duplicate and pass out the official handout on the following page.

Materials

- "HUG-A-TREE AND SURVIVE," following
- Loud whistle
- Large black trash bag
- Scissors
- Aluminum foil
- Masking tape
- Pencil
- Props, as needed

HUG-A-TREE AND SURVIVE

1. **ALWAYS CARRY A TRASH BAG AND WHISTLE** on a picnic, hike, or camping trip. By making a hole in the bag for the face and putting it on over the head, it will keep the child dry and warm. The whistle will carry further than the child's voice, and takes less energy to use.

2. **HUG A TREE** once you know you are lost. One of the greatest fears a person of any age can have is of being alone. Hugging a tree and even talking to it calms a child down and prevents panic. By staying in one place, the child is found far more quickly and can't be injured in a fall.

3. **MY PARENTS WON'T BE ANGRY AT ME.** Time and again, children have avoided searchers because they were ashamed of getting lost, and afraid of punishment. Anyone can get lost, adult or child. If they know a happy reunion filled with love is awaiting, they will be less frightened, less prone to panic, and work hard to be found.

4. **MAKE YOURSELF BIG.** From helicopters, people are hard to see when they are standing up, when they are in a group of trees, or wearing dark and drab clothing. Find your tree to hug near a small clearing if possible. Wear a red or orange jacket when you go near the woods or desert. Lie down when the helicopter flies over. If it is cool and you are rested, make crosses or "SOS" in broken shrubbery, rocks, or by dragging your foot in the dirt.

5. **THERE ARE NO ANIMALS OUT THERE THAT WANT TO HURT YOU.** If you hear a noise at night, yell at it. If it is an animal it will run away. If it is a searcher you are found. Fears of the dark and of "lions and tigers and bears" are a big factor in panicking children into running. They need strong reassurance to stay put and be safe.

6. **YOU HAVE 200 FRIENDS LOOKING FOR YOU.** We have had children in the area of a search tell us, "My parents would never spend the money to search for me; why will all these people?" Of course, search personnel are professionals and volunteers who charge nothing and do it because they care. Many children who are lost don't realize that if they sit down and stay put, one of the few hundred people will find them. Some are afraid of strangers or men in uniform, and don't respond to yells, and have actually hidden from searchers they knew were looking for them.

7. **FOOTPRINTING YOUR CHILD** is a five-minute exercise that cuts down the time of a search by several hours. Have the child step on a piece of aluminum foil, on a soft surface such as carpeting or a folded towel. Mark the foil with the child's name. With this print, trackers can separate your child's track from the hundreds of others in the area, and quickly determine the direction of travel.

Adopt a Tree

Information ❧❧❧❧❧❧❧❧❧❧❧❧❧❧❧

Trees are divided into six main groups according to the features they have in common. *Broadleaf* or *deciduous* trees change into autumn colors, are bare in the winter, sprout buds into leaves and spring flowers which develop into fruits (oak, maple, birch, hickory). *Needleleaf,* also called *evergreen* or *coniferous* trees have needle-like or scale-like leaves and plain flowers that develop into seed cones or berries (pine, spruce, fir, holly, juniper). They do not lose all their needle leaves at once. *Palms* have huge leaves and no branches. They grow mostly in the tropics (royal palm). *Tree ferns* have no flowers, fruits, or seeds. They reproduce through spores (West Indies tree fern). *Cycad trees* flourish in warm, moist areas. Their cones grow up to three feet (.9 m) long and weigh about 100 pounds (45.4 kg) (South African cycad). *Ginkgo trees,* a single species group, bear strangely-scented seeds but no fruits or cones.

Project

Adopt a broadleaf tree and observe and sketch it over the four seasons; record the changes and draw conclusions.

Directions

1. Choose a deciduous tree and study it all year. Make journal entries about the tree on each visit.

2. With a magnifying glass closely examine the trunk. List the creatures that have made their homes there.

3. Sit quietly beneath your tree and listen to the sounds around you. Gaze up into its branches. What does the world look like from your tree's point of view?

4. Sketch your tree in each season on construction paper, noting changes and drawing conclusions about why those changes occurred. Try to explain how the plant knew it was time to drop its leaves, start to bud, produce its fruit, etc.

5. Cut each of your four seasonal trees out of construction paper. Cut out a fold-hinged door where each animal you observed lives. Glue the full length of the tree, except for the doors, onto a background sheet. Under each open door draw the animal that lives there.

Materials

- Botanist's Journal, page 6
- Magnifying glasses
- Construction paper
- Pencil
- Colored pencils or pen
- Scissors
- Glue

How to Plant a Tree

Information

In selecting a tree for planting, it is important to consider just the right tree and the right spot for your purposes. The best time for planting is when the tree is resting–early spring, winter, or fall. Trees with full leafy crowns make the best shade trees. Those that drop seedlings need to grow in an open grassy area for less cleanup. Consider how large the tree will be when it is fully grown and allow plenty of space. Pruning some of the extremely low buds will keep it from developing branches that hang too low. Look for fertile soil or work in a good planting mix. Be sure the planting area has good drainage so water does not collect and drown the roots. Keep the roots moist while they are out of the ground. The hole should be deep enough to allow room for all the roots to be below ground level.

Project

Plant a small tree on the school grounds in conjunction with Arbor Day activities, following.

Materials

- Small mulberry tree
- Shovel
- Burlap bag
- Potting soil
- Stake

Directions

1. Get permission before starting the planting part of this project.

2. Ask a local nursery to donate one or more mulberry trees. (They give marvelous shade and their leaves are great for silkworm experiments!) Volunteer to give the nursery credit in your classroom newsletter or photograph your project and submit an article to local newspapers for publicity.

3. Chart the steps of "How to Plant a Tree" and discuss them before actually planting any trees.

4. Write thank-you notes to the nursery owner.

How To Plant A Tree

1. Dig a hole big enough to spread out all the roots with none close to the top of the hole.

2. Pile the less fertile soil on one side. Mix some with potting soil and pile on the other side.

3. Insert the stake for support near the center of the hole, pushing down to anchor well.

4. Plant the tree by carefully spreading the roots out deep in the hole, being sure not to crowd them.

5. Cover the roots with the rich soil mixture and top with the less fertile soil. Tie the tree with wide ties that won't cut into the tree.

6. Wrap the trunk with burlap for the first two years to protect it from insects and sunburn.

7. Use a moderate watering schedule the first year.

Arbor Day

Information 🕊🕊🕊🕊🕊🕊🕊🕊🕊🕊🕊🕊🕊

In the mid-1800s a New England educator named Birdseye G. Northrop encouraged people to beautify the countryside by planting trees around schools, hospitals, churches, and along roads and highways. Prizes were given to groups and individuals who planted the most trees. The people of Nebraska planted over a million trees on the first day. Soon Arbor Day became the official day set aside for planting trees. School children and youth groups take the holiday very seriously. They not only plant lots of trees, they also assume responsibility to protect and care for their trees over time.

Project

Prepare for and invite parents to an Arbor Day Tree Planting Ceremony.

Materials

- Construction paper
- Crayons or markers
- Pencil
- Colored pencils or pen
- Scissors
- Glue
- How to Plant A Tree, page 45
- Hug A Tree, pages 42-43

Directions

1. Use craft materials to design individual invitations to an Arbor Day Tree Planting Ceremony. Send home at least two weeks before the event.

2. As a group, decide on a program for the day, using How to Plant A Tree and Hug A Tree pages.

3. Plan and prepare a Plant Feast (page 47) to serve your guests.

Plant Feast

In small groups plan and prepare a feast of plant foods.

Equipment

- Clear plastic glasses
- Baking sheets
- Serving spoons
- Paper plates
- Napkins
- Serving bowls
- Plastic forks
- Paper bowls
- Straws

Plant Pita

- Pita bread
- Bean sprouts
- Jicama slices
- Lettuce leaves
- White mushroom slices
- Green pepper strips
- Celery slices
- Carrot slices

Cut and stuff pita bread with an assortment of plant foods

Ants on a Log

- Celery sliced in two-inch (5-cm) lengths
- Peanut butter
- Raisins

1. Spread peanut butter into the hollow of the celery piece.
2. Top with several raisin "ants."
3. Place on a paper plate and serve.

Off-the-Tree Salad

- Apples
- Oranges
- Grapes
- Pineapple
- Kiwi
- Pears
- Bananas
- Orange juice

1. Slice fruits into a bowl.
2. Pour orange juice over all to maintain freshness and refrigerate until ready to serve.

World Wide Web

Look in the world wide web to expand your knowledge of the plants. Keep in mind that web pages change constantly. The web pages below were active at publication date but their continued presence is not guaranteed. Like the plant world, however, the world wide web is constantly growing, just ripe for young horticulturists to make exciting discoveries.

Address	Content
www.sarracenia.com/faq.html	*Carnivorous Plant FAQ*—everything you ever wanted to know about carnivorous plants.
gardening.com/	*Gardening.com*—Plant Encyclopedia, plant problem-solving, and a Garden Site Directory.
aggie-horticulture.tamu.edu/kinder/index.html	*Aggie Horticulture Just for Kids*—hosted by the Dept. of Horticulture Sciences, Texas A & M University. Includes topics of nutrition and composting, just for kids.
www.sci.mus.mn.us/sln/tf/d/dandelion/dandelion.html	*Dandelion*—part of the Science Learning Network/Science Museum of Minnesota *Thinking Fountain* site. Links to other plant and science sites.
www.amfor.org/bigtree/bigtree.html	*The National Register of Big Trees*—statistics on the record-holding trees all over the United States.